GREEN, RED, GOLD

GREEN, RED, GOLD

A Novel in 101 Sonnets

William Radice

FlambardPress

First published in Great Britain in 2005 by Flambard Press
Stable Cottage, East Fourstones, Hexham NE47 5DX

Typeset by BookType
Cover design by Gainford Design Associates
Printed in Great Britain by Cromwell Press, Trowbridge, Wiltshire

ISBN 1 873226 78 0

Flambard Press wishes to thank Arts Council England
for its financial support.

website: www.flambardpress.co.uk

Flambard Press is a member of Inpress
and Independent Northern Publishers.

Sonnet No. 7 was published by Kevin Perryman
in *Babel XIII*, Denklingen, Germany, 2003,
and is reprinted here with his permission.

to the ghost of my father

We are such stuff
As dreams are made on . . .

Prospero in *The Tempest*, IV.i.156–7

Song, let them take it,
For there's more enterprise
In walking naked.

W. B. Yeats, 'A Coat'

Every writer produces fiction to the extent that every
piece of writing is contrived.

M. T. Clanchy, *Abelard: a Medieval Life* (1997)

1

We're different. Sea and land. Watching the beach
This bright, still morning, where a downward stream
Catches the light while lapping wavelets reach
Gently upwards, I think to you I seem
Uncharted territory. So many paths and layers –
Languages, countries, books, my wife and daughters.
I've told you much – but how can all those years
Be yours? And then I stare at your calm waters.
You've let me peer down into dark and painful
Depths. I know them in part, but as if from a book
Of oceanography. I've seen no baneful
Monsters such as swim along paths you took.
    We're different. Yet, like stream and waves on shingle
    Catching the glancing light, our waters mingle.

2

One voice says, 'It's such a seductive road.
Complete it. Plough through the forest. Leave wife
And daughters and house behind. You'll be glad you strode
So bravely ahead to a new, quite different life.'
Another voice says, 'In marriage there's completion.
It's yours already. Sex, parenthood, home.
Not for nothing that link in Elizabethan
Thought – orgasm and death. It's gone when it's come.
Marriage is about extracting solace and love
From constant bereavement.' To which, 'You'll always be sorry
You left the road unfinished.' But, 'You'd grieve
For all that at present is safe from the builder's lorry –
    Flowers unpicked, eggs unhatched in the nest.
    Don't finish the road. Preserve the forest. It's best.'

3

Is touching too much? An embrace a dire disgrace?
Is a kiss as wicked as the fact I am writing this
Across the room from my wife? I touch your face,
Hands, legs, although you're not here. I miss
Your eyes, skin, voice. But even were you in my arms,
The purity of love imagined, not realised,
Would be unsullied. In theory, to picture your charms
Here, or savour them more than my wife has surmised,
Ought to be wrong. But it doesn't feel wrong. Why?
Even the deepest of kisses seems permissible.
It must be because untrammelled freedom to fly,
With full, physical wings, for us is impossible.
    Our flights are flights of thought. They harm no one.
    We cannot soar with Icarus close to the sun.

4

'*You* may need your wife's approval,' you said,
'But I do not.' True. You're free. And so
I keep asking myself, 'Why should my bed
Be denied you, supposing one day – and I know
I can never assume this – you yearned for it?
Why chain yourself to my scruples? Wear a chastity belt
My marriage has imposed?' But then I think for a bit
And wonder what, above all else, is felt
Between us. It's a longing to do what is good
And just and unharmful. It's knowledge of the pain
Caused through what by us so easily *could*
Be done, secretly, over and over again.
    Yet it's not fair on you. If only I could swerve,
    I'd give what you, by your goodness, more than deserve.

5

June rain. Most intimate of weathers. Everything
Lush and growing, but too wet for activity
Outdoors. Let gardening go. Let the world count for nothing.
Let this be a time for indoor unreality,
For discarding all consequence, all alteration to the rain,
Which hour upon hour will shelter me and you
From all return, all need to excuse or explain,
Its steady susurration hiding us from view
With the softest of blankets. Oh warm rain, if we don't
Have to face its coldness; merciful rain, if too
Unreal to stop; sweet rain, if whatever can't
Be done is, as it falls, allowed to be true.
    Rain that hides yet speaks, that conceals the real,
    Yet by that concealing makes so real what I feel.

6

Who says green eyes are jealous? Yours are clear
And open. You do not claim me. You do not narrow
Your gaze to cut out my wife. When your eyes come near
To mine, my own reflected blue should borrow
Some of your green, so I never tie you either.
And free of time we should be – our fluid blend
Of translucent blue and green should depend on neither
Past nor future, but instead should weave and bend
Like sea and cave-water married in Greek sunshine.
Is the blend in these poems? Please, linger and stare
Deep as if from a boat at each passing line.
Find, amidst fish and fronds and anemones there,
    Something undying, something scooped out of time –
    For your clear green eyes can be captured only in rhyme.

7

I vowed, 'If the end of our long wait comes, it will be
On Lindisfarne. Holy Island.' 'Why?'
You asked – but you knew, for your favourite place by the sea
Is a rock with a view of the flat land and high
Castle of Lindisfarne. Yesterday you took me there.
The light was milky, the waves stretched far and foaming,
The churning chill of the wind made me need on my bare
Arms the warmth of your body. The waves kept homing,
Pounding the pale yellow sand. They matched with their slate
Blue the blue-grey rocks. They seemed to keep pulling
The misty island towards us, dragging the weight
Of its castle, a holy vow of their own in the rolling
    Of each strong breaker – *If the wait gets too long to bear,*
    We'll carry the island to you through the wind-churned air.

8

Your worst monster is a void. You don't know who
Your father was. It must be like the loss of part
Of your visual field – but bleaker, because for you
It's never ever been there, and the void is in your heart.
How to trace him? Could there be leads in the Irish Club
In Newcastle, or in Ireland's West? As we talked, a plot
For a novel (if poems can be novels) hit me like a stab
Of fate. Suppose the search – connected to a short
Fling *my* father had in Newcastle – revealed you in the end
As my half-sister? Was *that* what had drawn us together?
In my novel, I now grip your hand, feel joined yet penned
By the wrong kind of ring. Better an unknown father
    Than be fenced by another taboo against two being one.
    In this, *my* void. A slice of my own heart gone.

9

I've told you about my headache, how it's ruled my life.
But it must seem even more than usually implausible
To anyone seeing me with you. For you wield a knife
In your deft, slim hands that can gently work the removal
Not perhaps of the headache itself but its aura
Of struggle and despair. There's a dance in the skill of those hands
As with the nimblest of surgeons. You're the best restorer
Of high spirits I've ever known. The lands
You have led me to – dancing up hillsides, twirling
Round and round as you would to an Irish jig,
Or moving as you do when we kiss – are the same unfurling
I sense in these sonnets: no mask, no pretence, no fog,
    But a clear vista of what I am meant to be.
    Such sunlit waves dancing. Such open sea.

10

You didn't find it clear, that one about the forest.
I've tried to make it clearer. The forest I could destroy
Isn't my marriage, it's the reward for being chaste.
Because our road can't be built, we're free to enjoy
The forest's untouched beauty – or so I tell myself.
But let me picture it further. My marriage built a road,
It reached a glade – a serene house – no wolf
Or monster to threaten it; for me a perfect abode.
My wife's career beckoned. She left. I failed
To follow. Unfair on her, I know, but this
Is the place where I breathe and write. Now it's filled
With sharing with you things she doesn't seem to miss –
    Poems, forest-walks. Do I still want her here?
    With a clear new road from the glade would the poem be clear?

11

There are things that we explore together that are too
Private even for these sonnets. My fundamentalist
Brother is different. When he asked me, 'How often do you
And your wife have sex?' I heard the same exhibitionist
Blast as on the trumpet of his faith. It made me think about
How sex and religion converge in intimacy.
I've never shared faith with my wife, while my brother can shout
About marrying in faith as well as virile sexuality.
His style isn't mine, but I agree to this extent:
With you I have a sense of shared faith growing
As well as potential sex. Maybe I'm meant
Never to know either in full. But with each kiss you're showing
    Me a mystery that maybe already holds me in its mesh.
      Deep in your mouth, you reveal how the Word was made flesh.

12

'I've never shared faith with my wife.' Is that fair?
There's a destiny we've shared, and a brave belief
In that destiny that's brought us, stair by stair,
To our present heights without serious grief.
And I've loved her each step of the way, and our daughters too.
But now I'm beginning to feel that we've been bound
Like soldiers in arms. The army's come under review –
The general's saying, 'Time to leave the high ground,
You've done your duty. Now you need to be free.
No need to climb any more, no need to strive.
Be yourselves. No one commands the leaves on a tree.
There's a time for orders, and a time for coming alive.'
    My wife and I made destiny our creed;
    But faith is unscripted – a start, a beginning, a seed.

13

There's a fuchsia bush in my garden – my favourite flower.
When it comes out I always think of the West
Of Ireland, where it grows in hedgerows. I had an hour
Before my journey to London – I wanted to rest
In your cream room and to be with you again.
I grabbed a spray from the bush on my way – greeted
You with it. You put it in a vase: it seemed to explain
More than any words could say – but what completed
Its beauty? What made its dark green leaves and pendulous
Blood-red flowers so perfectly matched? 'It's the stalk,'
You observed, 'it's red too' – and at once a tremendous
Joy swept through me at the way you think and talk.
    My lock, your key; an intense release of stress.
    My blood-mix matched by your Geordie Irishness.

14

When you kiss, you dance. Your legs and arms and body
Move and entwine like a dancer's, and make me dance
Too. Remember that dance we saw at the ballet?
Man and woman in a seamless spiral, advance
And response, coil and uncoil, an unfettered simulacrum
Of sex. But never pornographic, despite the bare
Breasts of the female. And now, as you fill the air
Around my pen, your legs astride the fulcrum
Of my loins, your breasts – though I haven't yet seen them uncovered
(That's against our rules) – very like that dancer's, to me
It seems love-making through dance cannot be bettered,
That the limit imposed on our love has set us free.
    When we watched that dance, we didn't want them to bring
    It to an end. Why end *our* dance with the real thing?

15

If you changed sex, I would still love you – and with
Your impish smile, boyish hair and lithe
Frame I feel I would only have to breathe
On you for you to turn into Prospero's blithe
Ariel. But was Ariel male? And where is gender
In a love that is celibate, pure, androgynous? Yet
It's not unphysical – any more than the tender
Stroking of a cat is unphysical. A cat
Introduced us. I found your cat dead by the road –
Couldn't find out whose he was, buried him prayerfully.
You heard – came round to thank me. Something flowed
Into me at that first sight of you, ethereally
    Lit by my French window. Girl? Boy? You'd still
    Be my tricksy spirit. I loved you at once. Always will.

16

To be Ariel is your defence. It keeps you free.
Even a Prospero cannot hold you. My art
In these poems, because it's yours, you can merrily, merrily
Discard if you want to. You're a creature apart,
And that is your magic. Yet Ariel doesn't have feelings,
And I know you do, as once I profoundly hurt you.
I promised the whole of me, mind and body. Like peelings
Of an onion you started to open up layers, let me view
The woman underneath. I let you down. When I cleaved
To my wife after all, you stung back, made me weep
At my blundering cutting of your skin. You foolishly believed
Me, because you're a woman, not a spirit. My remorse was deep.
    You forgave me. You restored your layers, again became
    Ariel. But as woman you're scarred, and I am to blame.

17

My wife and I went to Portsmouth, to sail with friends
Who have a boat. 'What *is* fibre-glass?' I asked the chemist
Husband. And then, when he'd explained, 'If blends
Of glass-fibre are opaque, why does transparency exist?
Why is ordinary glass transparent?' 'Because it's homogenous,'
He said, 'the same all through. Air and water
Are homogenous; they're transparent too.' That's analogous
To these poems, I thought, as the bright, white boats and brighter
Air and water held my gaze. Variety in
Sails and equipment, but their style is daylight and sea.
The same all through – no cloak, innuendo or grin;
No play-acting, leg-pulling poet this time – just me.
    Last time, mad pyrotechnics – flares in the dark.
    This time, the truth. Not one exclamation mark.

18

'Wind in her sails . . . sailing with the wind.' Metaphors
From the age before steam, when ships would mainly rely
On wind behind sail. I thought the same basic laws
Still applied – till my friend explained for a yacht to fly
Fastest a cross-wind was best. The sail made the wind
Different in speed on either side; the force
High to low pulled ropes that pulled the boat. Did I tend
To think of my wife as the wind in my sails – and curse
When she wasn't sufficient? But the best sort of wind comes
Crossways; the speed one side of the sail needs another
On the other. Have I, in you both, found the wind of my dreams?
One wind, two pressures? In the bright and gusty weather
    In which we sailed from the harbour, my wife looked at ease.
    No threat from your ghostly presence, smiling in the breeze.

19

When you'd read my fuchsia poem, you told me a story
Of your own about green and red. You were eleven.
You had to write an essay on you and your heritage. It was scary
When the teacher called you to the front – for you feared that heaven
Had been mixed in your essay with the body's nails and whips.
But the teacher was impressed, asked you to read it. *Where*
God kissed my head He left the red of His lips
So that in the sunlight you can see where His mouth brushed my hair.
It matched my green eyes and made me Irish. O God
Of accursed blood. You were taught He works to the good,
But much more real was the green yet blood-soaked clod
That made you what you are, not what you should
    Have been. O God of your and green Ireland's red;
    Of the saved, but also the pierced and scourged and dead.

20

Although the water's transparent, it's opaque
Deep down. When I peer far, the depths are dark,
Too dark even for these sonnets. You wrote: *Take*
My hand, let me lead you to the water's edge. Look
Into my dark depths. It was after the sequence began.
In your sea, the first sonnet made such waves
In the lonely night, such turbulence, you ran
Downstairs, wrote me a poem that now paves
Our love's bottom-most road, and always will.
A dark and fluid and shifting road – I can't
Walk firm on it, nor can you; and perhaps it would kill
Us if we tried – such monsters. I've promised I shan't
    Probe it in poems – no poem could ever do so.
    Too dark for light; a place where the truth can't go.

21

'Let's pretend.' Innocent children make
A game from what is adult, hidden, rude.
Can an adult secret that would break
Hearts if it were let out be imbued
With innocence by pretending that the real's
Unreal? Suppose two lovers, in a game,
Said nakedness was clownish garb, and squeals
Of ecstasy were free of sin and shame
As vaudeville that seeks to entertain,
And secrets were so free to public view
That naught in them caused shock or rage or pain.
They pray as they play this game, those naughty two,
    That God sees their imagined pantaloons
    And winks at acts performed by harmless loons.

22

'Play me a really beautiful piece,' you asked,
And I chose the Adagio from the Pathétique
Sonata. I'd practised; I played it well; I basked
In your loving listening, made the *cantabile* speak
With even more depth and passion the second time through –
And then felt tired. Artists are egotists,
It's said, and I myself know this is true.
But the ego needs to be big if it insists
On giving till it's spent. Artists are good
But bad lovers; they don't just take, they give –
They give – but often not the power and flood
That's made their art. Perhaps I was a sieve
    For Beethoven's self-giving when I played.
    His flood washed out the love I'd else have made.

23

But thy eternal summer shall not fade . . .
I didn't re-read Shakespeare's sonnets before
Starting these; but of course his ghost has stayed
Near, and his Man and Lady are at their core
As well as you. Northumberland summer. So brief
But yet so perfect. This summer is yours. As I sit
On the lawn and write, your hope and joy and grief
Are spread like a gossamer carpet, and you flit
This way and that, and my beating heart dances
With you. Oh will this summer be repeated? Or will
The gossamer turn to burning coals, and lances
Of shame puncture my heart, its blood to spill?
   Yet this summer is yours, outliving you and me,
    So long as men can breathe or eyes can see.

24

Celibacy, chastity . . . we've moved on and will move
Further still, perhaps. One day my wife
Will see these poems. When I first told her my love
For you might end our marriage, she played the hand of her life:
Said some triangles could be perfect; said I could keep
You as my friend; said she wanted me to be myself.
I've taken her at her word. Will the truth of it seep
In gradually? Will some benign angel or elf
Put blinkers over her eyes? Will the reality
Revealed in these sonnets spark off an inferno of shock
And horror and rage, consuming our marriage utterly?
Or will she find, within the flames, the unburnt rock
   Of love and fidelity? Is this why the guilt I should
    Feel doesn't bite? Am I doomed, after all, to be good?

25

The burning coals and the lances of shame have come
Quicker than I thought. My poetry was one step ahead –
It usually is. But the crisis has not come from
Exposure, but from knowing my future as your lover is dead.
There's a rock in the way. I thought you and I could sit
On it – as we did on your rock near Lindisfarne.
I thought that waves from what seemed like the burning pit
Of my marriage could become those sunny, rolling, clean
Sea-waves that were pulling the island towards us; but
My rock has remained not yours, and it will not burn.
I do not yet know if the road is now shut,
Back to your favourite rock. I shall always yearn
　　To return – to the cool wind, and the misty view
　　Of an island whose causeway is closed to me and you.

26

I sang and played you a song – not taking in
Its words till I'd got to the end. 'It's very sad,'
You said, and it is, and sadder still is my sin.
The water is wide, I cannot get o'er – I was mad
To think that I could – no wings, no boat – and you
Were mad too *to lean your back against an oak,*
Thinking that he was a trusty tree. Too true,
Too true, every word of that song – I cannot revoke
Anything – *love when it's old it groweth cold*
And fades away like morning dew – but I'm praying
That the dewy grass in my garden can still enfold
The jewel of my love, despite my stupid betraying.
　　It will be pure and holy; it will be these poems when I give
　　You them all; it will not grow old or cold; it will live.

27

We're lovers, yet we're not, and so our ploy
Must be to push towards a false conclusion:
Our myth of chastity to cunningly destroy
By meetings, sightings, jaunts in rich profusion.
Yet in these sonnets, by their tale of impotence,
I'll speak a truth that may yet seem a lie
To those who think my sorrow is pretence
And my intense confession but a sly
Device in what is much less life than art.
That wicked laugh of yours: had I but caught
Its tune, we might have not been forced to part
Our bodies; hence I'll match it in my thought –
   Make gay poetic trickery express
   Your lovely, lost, forsaken wickedness.

28

You showed me a photo of yourself at nineteen,
And asked, 'Would you have fallen for me then?'
Your hair had its coppery, Irish, God-kissed sheen,
And its reckless length must have trapped many young men
In its burgeoning, wiry curls. I do not know.
So different were our worlds. But better might
Have been my chance of grappling in one go
With the angel and devil in you – no choice, no fight,
But a flight by the same wings that worked as well
In hell as in heaven. Loving you now, I
Being married and you cut free of your curls and their spell
Of red, I find your wickedness passes me by
   (Except in your laugh). But it's not just your short hair.
   I'm also entranced by the Angel scent you wear.

29

The past tense now. You have written saying all
My sonnets will be returned. And tomorrow's outing is off.
This could well be the end. But you've left a chink in the wall.
You've signed your name with a cross. With you that's half
Kiss, half sign of the cross. Your note was headed
'Your mixed messages returned'. True. But the muddle
Has been yours too – or these poems could not have wedded
Us. Now I must patiently try to unravel the riddle.
It's best I do so alone. It's best that art
Takes over from life now. That way you're protected.
God forbid that I further invade your heart
By claiming these sonnets are you. They're best confected –
   No more you than the long earrings you favoured,
   Or your elegant clothes, or the Angel scent I savoured.

30

We never knew what it was. I called it love,
Because love's such a flexible word. But death is the measure
Of love – which deaths count most: mine wouldn't move
You as your cat's death did, and the only treasure
I have that would break me to pieces to lose are my wife
And daughters. Was it lust? Only at times,
And not enough for the fire to burst into lasting life.
It was more like a poem. We kept on finding rhymes.
From rhymes came images. Something shaped the whole –
It used our moods and lives with callous disregard
For others. It had no more of a moral goal
Than a stream or tree. It drove us both too hard,
   Made us less kind – so it now seems to me.
   A strange poetic encounter: my land, your sea.

31

Yes, the untouched forest would have been better.
We could have gone on roaming, admiring the flowers.
But my road-building urge was too strong. I forgot the fetter
That would stop me walking the road to become yours.
My marriage wasn't the fetter: that, if I cruelly
Chose, I could have broken. It was more the chain
That is a poem – link by link it must slowly
Reach full circle. Because it cannot wane
When finished, it can't grow either. It's not the rose
I brought you once, so red, so fragrant; it's
The rose's shape. In marriage, a rose that grows.
In one flesh, the vase in which it fits.
    You said, 'A perfect rose. I'm going to press
    It.' Harder to press the rose that poems express.

32

The last songs we listened to, by Hugo Wolf,
Had one in which the lover wished the house of his beloved
Was transparent as glass. You said you would yourself
Make a poem from that. Since then, each time I've hurried
Past your house, I've looked through its glass walls
And seen you – you seem as fragile as glass too,
And the walls trap you, and how it grieves and appals
Me to think I led you to think that, if we flew,
The roof of your house would lift, and your shining wings
Would carry you heavenwards, whereas in fact we've crashed
Back through the glass, and the pain of its splinters stings.
But maybe only in *my* mind is it smashed.
    Maybe you've trained part of you not to care.
    Maybe, behind the walls, you're not even there.

33

I told you, that last sunny evening on the pub terrace
(A distance between us growing, you later said),
That I thought you were wholly good. I think the chalice
I drink from is good too. It's because we're led
By Abelard and Heloise's 'ethic of pure intent'.
We both have dangerous demons, but were they to the fore,
We wouldn't have waited so long, nor, when we bent
Our rules too far, would we have slammed the door.
But good can be made of bad. Yours was the flood
Of your childhood; you almost drowned. I'm not scathed
Like that, but maybe I'm muddied instead with the blood
Of poetry. Snap. You and I are swathed
   In the same shroud. Poetry – goodness as well –
   Needs darkness. God needs sin. Heaven needs hell.

34

We should have – at least once before our rift –
Been naked. We should have re-enacted our last
Death before our present birth. If the gift
Of marriage was ours at the time, we must have passed
Together from that life to this. Because *we brought*
Nothing into this world, it is certain we carried
Nothing from before except that nakedness. To cavort
Like pagans in the rain would be best. To be married
For an hour amidst rain and grass and earth
Would be enough. The water on hair and skin
Would have connected the slippery exit of birth
With the flesh that is grass before a birth can begin.
   We would have discovered, embracing in June rain,
   That what we possessed before can't be had again.

35

These are scandalous poems. I may never live them down.
It is not just that they stem from infidelity.
It's not (trickier) the way they go to town
On sex and religion. It's not the cruel stupidity
(Worst) with which I led you towards prospects
I couldn't realise. It's more the way they strip bare
The divine body of the world. A poet inspects
It at his peril. Everything, layer by layer,
Is linked: good and bad, beauty and ugliness.
Religions try to clothe it – in garments of peace,
Hope, love. They fail to conceal the mess.
It's a sweating, shitting body. Yet the lucid grace
    Of your green eyes looks at it with dispassion. Will those
    Who absorb these poems see what your gaze knows?

36

We should have waited for the waves. They might not have brought
The island, but we should have waited. They were so reassuring.
They had such confident strength – nothing can thwart
The wind-urged waves of the sea, their crests, their pouring
Surf as they batter the beach with violence that's steady
And kind. Instead, I dragged *you*, made you swim
Through ice-cold, salty waters, each swirl and eddy
A nightmare, but worst of all the way your slim
And beautiful hands were scraped and bloodied and tattered
By the island's barnacled rocks, as we tried to heave
It towards us, while waves whose task it should have been battered
And pounded *us*, threw us in the end to pant and grieve
    On a shore reached before time, thus not our home,
    Not holy; a desolate world of fog and foam.

37

Too absent your father, too present mine. What
You would give to remember the grip of your father's hand
As I do the thick, warm hands of my father from cot
To horseplay to climbing trees to dusting off sand
On seaside holidays. And the warmth still in his old,
Limp hands after his stroke when he lay in hospital.
Who knows what *your* father's hands were like, whether cold
Or warm, roughened by labour, or trim and subtle
With Irish eloquence? My father acquired a stain
On his hands from betrayal; but now that I've found the same
Flaw in myself, I like them better again.
Were he here, I would squeeze them, acknowledge a bond of shame.
    Better that bond than your intractable fate:
    No chance to make peace, even when it's too late.

38

Will I gain, in the end, from the knife that friendship with you
Has applied to me? It's cut but it's also healed.
Do these poems copy that knife, taking their cue
Like a trainee surgeon from the dropping of *your* shield?
For you opened up layers you normally hide well away.
But which layers are happiest? You brought me release,
Only to open me up to further pain and dismay.
Did I do the same to you? It seems there is no cease
To the flaying, and the world too may be made like this:
Strip away barriers, and new, ecstatic reality
Briefly shines; but dig a bit more, and bliss
Gives way to torment, then escape, then loss, faith, nullity
    And so on, to and fro, light, dark, no knowing what
    Lies at the bottom, or whether it's loving or not.

39

That my wife and I live too much apart is my
Fault, and the same flaw in my nature has mauled
You. I say one thing ('By all means apply
For that job in London'), but almost at once I'm stalled –
Blocked from roads that I pushed you both along.
I can always find reasons – headache, conscience, work.
But there must be a deeper law. However strong
And decisive one tries to be, there's a quirk
In the scheme of things. A road may seem to be buildable,
But excavate, lay, roll, finish as one might
There's an obstinate, clogging, riotous lust in the jungle
That sprouts up through the tarmac and wins the fight.
    It's the law of no law: call it Nature's life-breath.
    Yet it's also the power behind powerlessness. Call it death.

40

Poetic words are orgasmic: the coming together
Of sound and sense. Their sound is their flesh – the world
Of lips, tongue, teeth and breath that, light as a feather
Or hard with biting passion, your kisses unfurled.
Our love gave me the noise of these poems: I write
Them like a song-composer inspired by your voice –
Geordie when it was manifest, soundless as night
When our tongues darkly met. But meaning is a force
Beyond the physical, beyond any language's sound.
Of this you've sung to me too: the deeper Word
Underlying our friendship – I perceived its shadowy ground
Wherever we were, whatever we did, whether we erred
    Or observed proprieties. It makes these poems come:
    Words and their sense unstoppably part of a sum.

41

My wife has returned – she's doing unscripted things,
Finding new ways for us to unite again.
It's very strange. It's as if she not only brings
A clean sheet on which to paint with no pain
New flowers, but as if the many pages beneath
Have somehow lost their ugliness. I look
For dead trees, for blight, for a funeral wreath –
But suddenly all such things have gone from the book.
'I don't want just to be therapy for
Your marriage,' you said to me once; the role implied
That after the cure you wouldn't figure any more.
But leafing now ahead through the book, wide-eyed,
    I find *your* paintings of green trees from my past.
    No sign of their ever fading. The green holds fast.

42

Ever since getting to know you, the word 'grace'
Hits me in anything I read. For example, *The Tempest.*
Banquet whisked away so that three men face
Their sin: *Bravely the figure of this Harpy hast*
Thou perform'd, my Ariel; a grace it had devouring;
Or the *soft grace* of patience, whose aid must make
Irreparable loss curable; or Caliban's glowering
I'll be wise hereafter, and seek for grace. To wake
From purgatory is grace, so the play shows. You've shown
Me that yourself, each time I've done you wrong.
But never would I have done so, had I known
The purgatory that's made your grace so strong.
    No grace in me till after my poet's slog.
    Art must be dropped, as in Prospero's Epilogue.

43

Our dance – had it remained a dance – would have been
Like that fuchsia. Or like it, rather, had it stayed
Forever in the vase in which its green
And red, quivering, complex beauty played
With the sunshine in your cream room like your lips
On mine. My clumsiness as a dancer tossed
That dream away. Frailty's punishing whips
Slashed the fuchsia's delicate blooms; they lost
Their sheen; they shrivelled. Yet I imagine grace
In your throwing out of the fuchsia – tenderness,
Forbearance in your distant-seeing face.
Even as trash, here was a thing to bless:
    The faltering dance of the fuchsia's blood-soaked stem,
    Wilting with what true grace does not condemn.

44

When I cast you as Ariel, less harm
Seems done. If I turn spirit-like as well,
Become a bird, a chick, with dainty charm
I safeguard what was ours, and keep its spell.
So let me not be human; I'll be air,
Then to the elements we'll both be free.
There's love that has no taint of lust, no fear
Of loss to mar its calm androgyny.
For if as man and woman we had to part,
The fissure left a space – in which my hand
And yours, with no involvement of the heart,
Can meet without possession or demand.
    If there we touch, it will be with a feeling
    Of finding in the empty air a healing.

45

I liked cooking you meals. I liked telling
You to sit and watch while I sliced onions and cleaned
Potatoes. It was better when the only tears welling
Came from onion juice. I felt unweaned
From the safest kind of mother-love – I used
Skills copied from my mother. You said it was such
A pleasure to have a meal cooked for you. I refused
To let you help. The giving meant so much –
We ate and talked so happily. Can this go on?
Not as often – that was what brought me down.
But step by step, perhaps, our meals can run
On and up like a ladder's rungs to the crown
   Of love I so much wanted you to wear.
   Its gold was in your smile. It's still there.

46

These poems may not all be true, but I want
Their fabric to be truth. They may not all
Speak goodness, but the course they sail should be bent
On goodness. They may in recalcitrant details fall
Short of beauty, but like a sailing boat
With its gadgets and clutter they should, taken as a whole,
White sails flapping in the sunshine, proudly afloat,
Breasting with insouciance the heave and roll
Of the waves, tug truth and goodness and beauty
Into harmony, strenuous though that is as the work
Of sailing, the hauling of ropes, the obstinacy
Of current and wind against rudder; but I cannot shirk
   The task once started; the wind demands it; out
   Of sea, boat, sail must come the voyage I'm about.

47

In a pained letter you wrote, 'I'm not a character
In a novel or in one of your poems. I'm a real person.'
I know, but the ruthless yet also mitigating factor
In these sonnets is that you, when we're both dead and gone,
Will live in them *not* as the real you but as a ghost.
In an earlier letter you wrote, 'I'm bigger than my life.'
I know that too, and racing from coast to coast,
And driving the weather like the wind, and leapfrogging strife
And failure, and sweeping round the globe like sunrise,
You'll be a cloud-topping, peak-hopping ghost, and others
Will love you as I have done, and your all-seeing eyes
Whether open to the light or closed when our kissing smothers
 Them blankly, will keep on tracking real human loves
 Like a spotlight that, when the dancers move, moves.

48

I remember how when I was about thirteen the school
Doctor tested me for colour-blindness. There were numbers
Hiding in dots. Red and green made a fool
Of me: 'partial red and green blindness'. It encumbers
Me not in the slightest. I can read traffic lights.
But maybe more subtly I can't tell red/green apart.
And maybe you can't too – which is why our sights
Homed in on each other. It's the blood of the heart
And the wires of the mind; it's gunfire *and* it's green,
Serene detachment; it's the death-driven moral law
And the blithe life-spurt; it's sex *and* the epicene
Sexless love of all saints; it's the slamming of the door
 And the glimpse through the door. Maybe if I had seen
 That number, I wouldn't now mix the red and the green.

49

'What are you writing?' my wife quietly asked.
On the back of my page was a draft: her long-sighted
Eyes had read it. So what I had carefully casked
(Carelessly, rather – did I partly *want* to be indicted
By sitting so close?) had to come dribbling out.
Not all, and she didn't ask for it all; but enough for her to know
Of our meetings after we'd split; which cast some doubt
On the second, more drastic break I told her of now – and so
Forth. A bad evening and night and day
Followed. She couldn't stop crying. I kept thinking
Her tears were like ink from my pen, and to wipe them away
Was impossible. She's all right now. But the times of sinking
    You've known must have left you with far inkier tears.
    You see them daily in the mirror. The stain never clears.

50

Our love could be a fantasia. It could build
Such intricate variations on its theme
That the theme would be undetectable. Whatever's trilled
And veiled and ornamented might to our conscience seem
Innocuous. Neither God nor my wife would mind. We'd meet
As friends, and break no bounds. We'd play like two
Musicians – each committed to the complete
Thrill of the piece – flying wherever it flew,
Flaunting its flurries of notes like elaborately jewelled
Dancers. We could put on costumes to match – we could flash
Scarves and feathers and robes; we'd forget what had fuelled
The fantasia – it would ride on its own élan and dash.
    We'd be private, but not secret; we would take pride
    In deceiving no one, in having nothing to hide.

51

The Northumberland coast is dangerous for me: too mystical.
It's safer here in Whitby. Low-water sand
And cloudless skies have brought out commonsensical
Yorkshire family life in force. I planned
The ruined abbey – and no doubt my wife and I
Will see it tomorrow: and St Hilda, the date
Of Easter, the Northumbrian king's decision to apply
Roman not Irish rules will interrelate
Whitby and Lindisfarne. But not yet,
And maybe better never. A poet should visit
Yorkshire from time to time, and I mustn't forget
My mother was from Hull. You too have your share of grit.
    Let's stroll one day by Whitby's homely sea;
    Watch the families; laugh at our madness in 2003.

52

'Sex is an all day thing,' you said to me once
During that brief time when we thought we'd indulge in it:
The planning of each approach, position and advance,
The mental rehearsal. Now that I sublimate it
In the form, say, of piano music, I rehearse
Physically, perform in various styles
From precise Bach to showtime kitsch or worse,
From Chopin's bravura to Mendelssohn's gentle wiles.
I play as your lover; but maybe as time goes on
You'll become in my mind like the noble Abbess Hild,
Drawing out songs of praise from humble Caedmon.
I'll sleep in the stable, and dream, and then be filled
    With a great song of Creation for your sake.
    To you I'll be a monk; a sacred love will wake.

53

The mist did it – swathing the bare ruined choir
Of Whitby Abbey; connecting it with Jarrow
And Lindisfarne; kindling again the religious fire
That stopped the Northumbrian saints being chilled to the marrow
By their bleak outposts; burying modern Yorkshire's
Fish and chips and booze in stoic prayers;
Subsuming my East Riding mother into what in those years
Was *North-Humber-Land*; delving to layers
In *you* that were laid by King Oswy's kingdom – the fusion
Of Irish and Roman and Geordie; miring
My Irish, Italian, London and Northern confusion
Of birth, youth, middle age and mortal expiring
    In a swamp of black-night-mist where my fire will die,
    Consumed with that which it was nourished by.

54

Ancestry is infinite – the whole of the human race.
So why not find pieces of myself in Abelard,
And you in Heloise? Neither in love nor disgrace
Are we comparable, but we face, as they did, a hard
And long struggle to change one kind of relationship
Into another. You're honest like Heloise,
And tough – you practise your faith, but when you slip
From conviction, you shrug as you rise from your knees.
I have something of Abelard's pride, vanity,
Self-pity, self-deception, cockiness, jesting impulsiveness.
He prodded religion with logic; I use poetry.
He was less wise than Heloise; hurt her with heartlessness.
    Yet they managed, in the end, to make their story complete –
    To rhyme, in friendship and work, with the Paraclete.

55

The Arden editor has fun with 'nothing'. For Hamlet
It's between maids' legs; so in Sonnet 12 it can breed
'Gainst Time's scythe; yet it's the pricking out
Of the master mistress in 20, to meet the need
Of a female *or* male lover. I, for my part,
Turned out to be nothing to you, and lesbian love
Might indeed be best for us, were we ever to start
On a physical course again; but that would prove
Impossible as well as wrong, because I'm a man
And you're not a lesbian. The jewel I therefore seek
Must be the nothing between us with which we began:
The sexual nothing, with nothing to screen or break
    The core of the jewel from shining eternally bright –
    Though the core is nothing without some other light.

56

There's a crossover coming. I didn't when I started this sequence
Know it would come. Perhaps you knew more. After
The first twenty-two, you dismissed them all as pretence –
Wrote it was quite clear 'who they were meant to honour'.
Yes and No. Wait. The moment of crossing
Will be where our laughter met – our carnival time,
Your allure, my camp poetics: a leaping and prancing
By you as the Principal Boy, with me as the pantomime
Dame. No need to remove your costume (your tights
With a seam down the back and red high heels
Are perfect), but I must work down from self-loving flights
(Pink frilly knickers) to what a victim feels
    (A poisoned robe). Honouring her, yes,
    But you no less, with honesty, wholeness, nakedness.

57

Can good be a greater temptation than bad? I fear
My weakness for kindness, loyalty, love. It kept
Me from being your demon lover; it made me steer clear
Of anything wicked in you that your courage had swept
Back into the dark past from which it had come.
It made me prefer not your coppery teenage curls
But your adult, self-disciplined crop; and when you looked glum,
The tears that had made the lines on your face were pearls
Of wisdom to me. The good in my wife too
Is what draws me so deeply, with physical fire you couldn't
Arouse, because it would savage the good in you
And my wife – leave both of you burnt not warmed. I shouldn't
    Fear goodness. The path, though, it has sometimes led
    From poetry, energy, mystery, fills me with dread.

58

The Arden editor notes that the Dark Lady
Sonnets number 28 – the female menstrual
Cycle. There are numbers also in my methodology,
And they're all prime: 29 up to our debacle;
Another 29 for the aftermath; a third 29
For the swapping of pronouns; 13 for the peroration
Plus 1 for luck to draw a line-zero-line
Under this prime number year. A mathematician
Has written a book on *The Music of the Primes*.
They 'represent the careful dynamic between
Chaos and order'. As do a poet's rhymes.
I trust this dynamic music: it's helping the red/green,
    Kiss/cross, angel and demon, light/dark, sea and land,
    You and her take me to truths I can understand.

59

To reverse the pronouns is hard. The subjects and themes
Are forming in my mind, but to make 'her' 'you'
And 'you' 'her' is a wrench not only in the stream's
Course so far but is also perilously new
For my poetry and for my faith. You matched my poetic
Demon; so easy to leave my poetry to him.
To discard him means standing alone behind a noetic
Wall with no chink admitting fancy or whim
Or amoral callousness. Yet the ground inside
The circular wall – real, experiential,
Baldly, painfully factual – mustn't override
Poetry. Deep underground it will lurk. Reverential
   My leaving of it there as I focus on real life:
   Discovering the woman in you by cleaving to my wife.

60

I go abroad sometimes, but return to our ground,
The ground of our past. To memories such as my arrival
At your hospital bed, my trousers and shoes browned
With Calcutta's mud, the blank of the non-survival
Of our first child my only thought throughout
The flight home. That loss, after thirty-three weeks,
Of what we never saw, and still can't talk about,
Connects us even more than our daughters. Silence speaks
For that child: it needs no words. You had the pregnancy;
I had the telegram, the rush to rearrange flights,
The dash through a monsoon tempest. Yet the vacancy
Was shared, and still is. Shared as our bed and our nights.
   I should have thought of this when my friend spoke of gaps
   In her life. I would then have treated her better, perhaps.

61

I had a scheme: each poem in this twenty-nine
To hark back to its counterpart in the First
And Second Acts. But reality's a vine
You can't completely train, and the grapes that burst
In my mouth as I write are not quite of my choosing.
Our home comes to my mind, and my friend's home
Too: she would ask me in – I wasn't abusing
Her privacy, I thought, yet I was, for whenever she came
To our house with you away, the altar of her cream
Room and family photos could not be reciprocated,
Because the home we've made is *our* life, *our* dream,
Our work, books, pictures, parenthood: violated
    Not by her but by me. Bitter the juice
    As I bite not only on your but on her misuse.

62

The world is a roaring plane. You and I, so far,
Have sat quite snugly behind our seat-belts. But
The massive machine would explode, kill, char
If it fell, and at any time it could, and that is the lot
Of victims of war and mayhem. I think when a plane
Takes off almost everyone aboard prays; and the instant
It lands, they all give thanks that they're safe again.
I remember returning from India with you and our infant
Daughters. When we landed, I clasped your hand. You smiled.
Safe so far. But anything can happen any time –
To many people it does. Life has propelled
My friend, at times, close to a crash. My sublime
    Imaginary flights with her have nothing to do
    With the vulnerable prayers she murmurs like me and you.

63

To be two can be lonelier than one. I used to long
To give my friend companionship, because
I felt she was so alone. But she said, 'I'm strong.
I don't want pity.' And now, especially when I'm yours
In bed, in our big, quiet house, our daughters gone,
It's as if we're alone in the universe. The dark outside
When we touch is frightening; but when I'm the sole one
Here, the vast spaces are kinder – they provide
Voices, friends, lights – and perhaps for my friend,
Alone in her bed, there's the same warmth and solidarity:
To drag her into a friendship with me was to rend
The embrace of the world. God must be terribly lonely.
    I worry that, loved by human beings, he might
      Be lonelier still. Leave him. Stick to what is right.

64

Marriage is about the reality of nakedness.
There are phases: discovery and passion; protection
And intimacy; then, with the years, sagginess, blotchiness;
Ending, perhaps, with incontinent dereliction –
Love surviving, if it can, all the way through.
My friend and I were never naked together:
I'm glad, for your sake, of that. But more true
Both to you and to her I'd have been if the weather
That lashed naked King Lear could have ripped off my lendings,
If my clothes of fantasy, poetry, mystical duplicity
Had been tossed aside – and instead of pretendings
She could have seen not a poet, not a weird multiplicity
    Of roles, but a single walk-on, walk-off part
      Which you, only you, have been able to learn by heart.

65

The morning after my friend and I disastrously
Crossed the line, I looked in the mirror and saw
Blood in my eye. A burst blood-vessel, probably.
Within a day it had cleared. Times of war
(And love) bring various kinds of blood to the eye.
Fighters see red. The wounded bleed and weep.
In those who do not have to kill or die,
But who find reasons and excuses, there's no seep
Of blood to cloud their righteous vision, unless,
When they study their eyes in the mirror, they're lucky to see,
As I did then, a murderous, bloody mess.
It's there in men more than women, though usually
   It's hidden. Often there's fire in your grey-blue eyes,
   But they're free of such blood. My friend's eyes likewise.

66

'What colour are your eyes?' I asked you after writing
Yesterday's sonnet. 'Green,' you said. I peered
More closely. Maybe a touch of green lighting
Their grey-blue. Colours have always appeared
More vaguely to me than to you. If I looked once more
At my friend's green eyes, would I see a touch of the hue
That reminds me now of that mad day on the shore
Near Lindisfarne – the wind-battered grey-blue
Of the sea and the rocks? Whose eyes are whose? It only
Matters that yours are warm and happy, that hers
Too one day if I meet her again should not look lonely
Or pained, should see in me nothing that stirs
   Suspicion. Let me be sun, rock, wind in the eyes
   Of you both, reflecting what's true in me, not lies.

67

You told me something about your father I'd never
Heard before. You were fifteen. Your exam
Results had turned out worse than anyone could ever
Have guessed. Especially English. They shattered your dream
Of becoming an Oxford don. You might have expected
Comfort from your father, but instead he raged and roared.
Your mother, cowed too, left you unprotected.
For weeks at Sunday lunch your tears poured.
Your brother and sisters were baffled, aghast. Your father
Is not a bad man. He denies any recollection.
'She's hardly likely to invent it, dear,' your mother
Says. For you, what he did still warps his projection
    Of kindness. So three fathers have caused desolation.
    My friend's blank. My loss. Your humiliation.

68

It's puzzled me that my headache has never interfered
With my potency. Maybe, in fact, there's a link.
My friend – on our happiest days – virtually cleared
Me of headache; I've shameful reason, however, to think
She might, had we gone on, have snipped my virility
Too – that the knife that her beautiful hands applied
To my forehead would have brought the same possibility
As Abelard gained when men burst in and made
Him *a eunuch for the kingdom of God's sake*. I wonder
Now about a further link – head,
Prick, poems; that the mystic raft of poetry under
Me and my friend would soon have sunk like lead
    If I'd stayed; that to give both her and my poems their due
    My head must ache, as it potently does with you.

69

Life in death is dependent on death in life.
I've learnt that with you. The house our marriage has built
Is for dying as well as living. No peace without strife,
Sex without shrivelling, mercy without guilt.
It's like the seasons. We've had to pass through winter
To find, again, the spring. With my friend it was all
Summer, so its shattering seemed to splinter
All hope of renewal. This must be what the Fall
Means – not the enriching autumn I know
With you, but the dark side of immortality:
Not life, but not death either. In order to grow,
Friendship, like marriage, needs death's repeated finality.
    Its absence seals under glass that I can't now mend
    Those flowering woods I once explored with my friend.

70

Beware of deep kisses – the way they replace
Words with the Word. Too dark and mushy, too yielding
Of self and will and wit to a cavernous space
Whose power we cannot control. Better the wielding
Of words of our own – in daylight outside the lips,
Not lost behind them. That's why you and I
Use lips not tongues for kisses and revel (since quips
And teases sparkle between us again) in wry
And merry exactness of words that bloom in the air
Like petals. The root's best left alone. My friend
And I probed too far down. There's nothing there
That's human. It brought our talk to an empty end.
    Maybe one day I can banter with her once more –
    In the light and air outside her lips' door.

71

In the unpredictable disposition of its greenery
A tree is free. And so are we – but the difference
Is that we must consciously build our harmony,
While the tree sings without trying. Last night, the expense
Of a carpet ordered for the flat we've bought to make
Our London life easier, which now you say
May be too big for the room, kept me awake.
'It'll have to go back,' I raged at dawn. 'No way
Can we turn down an edge.' 'Trust me,'
You said as you left for work, 'I'm good at these things.'
You are. That's why we've grown a flourishing tree.
You know how to fix the leaves. The tree sings.
    I've sometimes been deaf to that music, sought it elsewhere.
    But faith (I'm learning) means trust in each other's flair.

72

I never fully saw your beauty's grace
Until I told you of my wish to leave
You for my friend. It shone so in your face,
In your limbs as you sat on the sofa. It's why you achieve
So much at work. If snags arise, you hit
On solutions like those sofas, which you selected
So well for the room, and also now to befit
With their breadth of cream fabric our resurrected
Marriage. And thinking of this further, I see
Grace in the rooms you make wherever we live,
Which give, by their liberal beauty, space to me
And to you too in which to err and forgive.
    There's hard work in a grace so uncontrived.
    My friend's grace too. I saw how she worked for it. Strived.

73

We once saw some haunting puppets from Georgia.
You were too tired from your job to take them in.
I was transfixed. I loved the gaunt spectre
Of the puppeteer behind, his pallid skin
And dark clothes, the reverence of his handling
Of puppets patched and battered. I remember a scene
In a bar, a tipsy couple petting and dancing.
My friend doesn't drink – that gave an innocent sheen
To our times together: I felt we were like those blithe
Puppets, doing whatever our looming handler
Required, and not for real either. To writhe
Unaided is harder. Actual love and terror.
    The effort and risk of dancing undirected.
    Human, staggering steps; not God-perfected.

74

Her birthday last week. I sent her a card and a letter;
Then felt sick with worry I'd done the wrong thing.
I can cope with an end to touching – we've learnt we're better
Without it – it's not that kind of love. But the sting
Of knowing her to be there, down the road, and never
To see her again, would be more than I could bear.
It would be like the death of the sky; it would sever
Me from flight and breeze and birdsong. Air
Would become a poison; I'd choke on every breath.
Her answer came: normal, friendly – a chance
To believe afresh in rapturous flight from death,
With no trapped air this time, no bubble to lance;
    A leap to untroubled love, from new safe ground,
    And hallowed by Northern skies, and the birds' sweet sound.

Getting up in the night, and stunned by a brilliant show
Of moonlight, I wondered: should I take my cue
From the language of madness, from King Lear – *O!*
Well flown bird; i' th' clout, i' th' clout: hewgh! –
To give me words for what's so achingly arduous?
You, she and reversal: they provided ropes
To haul myself along between God the darkly perilous
And rational good; between storm-bashed slippery slopes
And self-responsibility. What words now
For this weird convergence, the ropes beginning to twine
Into one thick cable – rasping my hands as I plough
On to a place where opposite loves combine –
    'You' becomes her *and* you – and a song of sadness
    And gladness grasps at the moon for *reason in madness?*

'She's like Cordelia,' I said to my friend about you.
'She cannot heave her heart into her mouth.'
The more I think about this, the more it's true.
I'm not King Lear. You're wife, not daughter. But the drouth
That withered our marriage for a while stemmed, like Lear's
Torment, from my self-love, from my not perceiving
That nothing can mean everything. Then, in the tears
That rained through your smile's sunshine, I saw your grieving
Love; you were regal and patient, the calm of uncommon
Realism steadied you, yet *the holy water*
From her heavenly eyes that makes a vulnerable woman
(When Lear on his wheel of fire beholds his daughter)
    A spirit, made one of you; the same blend
    As in the sunshine and rain of my best friend.

77

When we went sailing, you were there, but present
Too in my mind was my friend; and now when I think
Of you both as spirits you become the gay, exultant
Rush of the boat itself; but watch – on the brink
Of madness – how the cross-wind that drives
Us so fast becomes all too often in this violent world
A bomb that rips the sail, a missile that dives
To the keel and holes and explodes and suddenly, hurled
On the waves are body parts, yours and hers, so precious,
Their blood making blue water green; it sends me insane
To think of how a crown of love's more glorious
The more the head that wears it is mortal; pain
 Articulates spirit; a cross conveys a kiss;
 Cordelia, soon to die, is *a soul in bliss.*

78

Howl, howl, howl. Were I King Lear;
Were Cordelia not just you, not my friend, not one
Of our actual daughters, but this whole mortal sphere
Carried limp in my arms, forever gone
And dead as earth; I'd howl at blood that pours
From the sky, as it does on our rowan tree this season,
And at blood spilled in return, in horrors and wars;
I'd howl at the bloody cross revealed by reason,
With its vertical pointing to deathless green, but slicing
Across it the clamping, crushing crime of the red.
This is where I find, in you and my friend, a splicing:
My drawing you nearer, poem by poem, has led
 Me to see, in you/her/all for whom I howl,
 Spirit pledged to its own murder foul.

79

I must step back; I'm floundering. When my friend spoke
Of her dark depths, she meant, I thought, biography.
I've kept clear of that. But the fires that now I stoke –
Too smoky to see – lick round the murky geography
Of spirit and world mixed; when I tried to make
You both inhabit that place, caverns gaped
For her, you and us all; hells that would break
All faith; cruelties, tyrannies, genocides, shaped
By the crossing of power and sinfulness, fire and dark.
Yet still convergence draws me; a rock where you
And she can safely rest. I must take a spark
From the blaze; cup it in my hand; shape it anew
    Into fire whose petals will gently keep you apart
    By growing from love – love for you both in my heart.

80

In some parts of the world the sun behaves
Itself, and this is one. Rarely too strong.
Courteously allowing sufficient rain. It laves,
As I sit, garden and house with warmth. I long
For you to be here. Your skin so loves the sun. My friend
Is fair-complexioned; she might choose shade, or the cool
Indoors. I thought, when I picked up my pen, I'd pretend
Our house (with the reds you chose for the bedroom wall
And the carpets) was you, and the green garden was her.
On a day like this, you are outside and she
Is in – but it doesn't matter, either can refer
To either, for the kind sun falls equally.
    Let me be, to you both, Northumberland autumn sun;
    But better – for in fact the sun ignores everyone.

81

She has sent me some photos. The best are of the day
She drove me to the coast. There is one of me sitting on cracked
Flat rocks, with the beach, the foaming sea and the grey
Of Bamburgh Castle behind me. I don't feel racked
With guilt at the sight: it makes me sturdily cheerful.
Draped on my knees, my hands look free and clean
As the milky waves and sky; subsequent fearful
Developments seem expunged by so serene
A photo – it allows me to be one
And the same man to you both: my stripy, long
'Matelot' T-shirt (chosen by you) fun
To wear with either of you; my enormous strong
    Walking-boots more a part of my life
    With her, but so what? Boots are no reason for strife.

82

I've bought, for the remaining batch of sonnets, a smart
Red notebook, and I'm writing with a green pen –
But not green-inked; if I'm to find in my heart
A love for you both that's free of deception, then
The ink should have no pigment – I want none
Of the interference that makes a mix of red/
Green paint muddy brown, but only the light of the sun,
Which when from an image red and green are transmitted
Together appears as yellow; moreover (so
My encyclopædia tells me), it's only when blue
Light is absorbed that red and green can flow;
So I offer my bright blue eyes to both of you,
    In the cause of a radiant glow that's not connected
    With ink, but is joy – joy of the Word resurrected.

83

'Will you take a pilgrim staff?' somebody quipped
When I said I planned to walk from Beal. No,
I didn't, but I crossed by the sand, not the causeway, and slipped
And slithered when I rashly decided to go
Across swampier parts barefoot. The burden
Of books in my rucksack – and of a boot (they're really
Huge) in each hand – should have earned me a pardon
For sin, but I felt guilt-free, and even more queerly,
My expected lonely, self-mortifying trip
Without my friend acquired a zest and merriment:
As if I was nearing, with every squelch and slip,
A place where she was already completely present,
    And you as well – the woman and spirit in each
      Of you separate, unmuddled, but jointly within my reach.

84

The 'carpet pages' – they struck me at once when I went
To the Priory Museum: those pages of astonishing
Ornament facing the start of each Gospel, meant
(According to the book I bought) as a sacred preparing
Of the ground for prayer, just like the prayer-mats
Of Islam; at once the Coptic-cross-bookmark
My friend brought me from the Vatican *and* our flat's
Bokhara carpet burst into bloom from a spark
In my heart. From now on, everywhere I turn
On Holy Island, I'll see inklings and emblems
Of you and my friend – as, for example, on page one
Of St John, red/green together in the arches of the 'm's
    Of *verbum*, the colours of the whole page being
      Green/red/gold, framed by the blue of my seeing.

85

In Bede's *Life of St Cuthbert*, a story moves me to tears.
It happened before his time on Lindisfarne
And Inner Farne. A beautiful youth appears
In the guest room of the monastery, tired and wan
As if from a night of winter travelling. Cuthbert
Greets him, washes his feet, says, 'Stay on
Till after terce, for some food.' A table is set.
Cuthbert goes to fetch bread. But the youth has gone
When he brings it, though no footprints mark the snow.
Taking the table back to the stores, the saint
Smells, then sees, three pure white loaves. 'Now I know,'
He says, 'the youth was a heavenly angel, sent
    To feed, not be fed.' My friend will be equally kind
    To me if she goes. She will leave three loaves behind.

86

My English teacher at school, now living in north
Northumberland, joined me today for a walk round much
Of the island. 'It's small,' he said as we sallied forth
Over grass and rocks and beaches, 'but it has such
Spaciousness – it seems like a whole world.'
This must be why I've come: for wholeness. To buy
A newspaper would be a crime. The air has unfurled
My headache, spread it out wide as the beaches and sky,
Too thin to feel. I float like a spirit, yet could –
I felt in bed last night – be a lusty lover
Here, to wife and friend. Mortality's good,
Frailty's sweet on this isle – I might discover,
    If I stayed forever, what it's like to be a honking seal,
    Or the *bar-tailed godwit* my teacher's binoculars reveal.

87

I've kept my vow, stayed away from my friend since our last
Bust-up. I may see her at the end of this week.
The sonnets will be finished. We cannot return to the past.
The love for you of which these sonnets speak
Is non-negotiable; but each step closer to the woman
In you has taken me closer to the woman in my friend,
And the spirit in my friend has widened its span
To you too. So I love you both without end,
My friend even more than before. It will be hard
Not only to let go of Ariel, but also the Cordelia
As present in her as in you. Goodness has barred
Me from hurting such beauty again. The isle makes me steelier,
   But also more potently amorous. Maybe that's why
    St Cuthbert returned to his Inner Farne cell to die.

88

Waking up this morning with my headache back, and thinking
That maybe I've lived long enough, and too many
More years would be ghastly, I find that the linking
Of you and her, red and green, that was honey
And harmony yesterday, today is the terror
Of Sonnets 77–79 again. Your meeting-place
Is the mud I slithered on weakly when I made the error
Of crossing the sands without boots; the monks would face
(I tell myself) cold and disease, not always know peace
And beauty, and never the comforts of this hotel.
Yet the island is holy. The way the tide without cease
Binds and liberates, tells me why heaven and hell
   Are equally possible when world and spirit combine:
    The water of giving; the mud of making you mine.

89

Giving, loving – there is no other right way.
It brings in the tide – makes the island whole and free.
Yet it also, when the tide goes down, and the sand of each bay
Is smooth and clean, and you can joyously see
Wader-birds in the shallows, and seals basking,
Makes reconnection with the world no nightmare.
And who 'you' are is no more for the asking,
For you are the object of all love everywhere.
I need a song – I've had it in mind since June,
An ancient song – *I'll sing you one O, Green*
Grow the rushes O – for I'm fond of its lively tune
And its pagan and Christian mix. I shall let it mean
 Nothing but giving, nothing but the sun-like glow
 That red and green – when I gaze humbly – show.

90

I began these poems as *the one who did not go to heaven.*
I cannot say if I've joined the eleven who did,
But even the one who didn't can be saved and shriven
If out of the mud on which my bare feet slid
Can grow a red/green fuchsia; gentle hands
Express the grace of its growth; their calm caress
Removes the pain in my head – flies me to lands
Where flesh joins spirit, not only me to bless,
But the whole of our mixed-up world. The café-garden
In which I write these lines is sunny, quiet,
Full of birdsong, flowers and butterflies – but the burden
Of the song runs through everything – murder, riot,
 Greed, hatred – if only we keep on listening,
 And even on darkest tears see light glistening.

91

Twelve for the twelve apostles. Think of me as loyal.
The fruit of the vine I harvest has sometimes been bitter,
And its roots are in dark and unfathomable soil.
But its branches reach towards the warmth and glitter
Of the sun. They embrace you both. When the ardent breeze –
As on the island this sun-kissed day – scores
Through them, their intricate melody wants to seize
You, as Eadfrith does when his vision soars
And wraps St John in patterns and shapes and hues
Of *quite exceptional exuberance . . . offering all . . .*
In a single, final tour de force. The views
On which I let my eager eyes now fall
    At the Heritage Centre, turning each 'virtual page'
    With a fingerstroke, are the fruit's ripe, gold stage.

92

I'm giving you the numbers of the song in a random order.
This seems to accord with my book here, *The Music of the Primes.*
The language of the book goes far beyond the border
Of my understanding, yet the random occurrence of rhymes
In poetry's language, the way, nonetheless, they're stairs
Climbing to harmony, makes me closely akin
To the mind of a mathematician. And anyone who stares
(As you can from this island) at *the seven stars in*
The sky, can gain, from their order and randomness, access
To the music that Riemann and others are sure must arise
From *the critical line* that makes the primes so patternless.
Proof is elusive – as in what's helped me devise
    These sonnets, one by one, at no fixed time,
    Following an infinite line, each one a prime.

93

A gracious, free-spirited American woman is here
At this B & B. I've suggested we meet for dinner.
I adore women. I want them to know no fear:
To be cherished, unbullied, respected. They don't see the sinner
In me that my God-mad brother would sternly condemn;
Even my philandering father was loved and forgiven
By all the women who shared a dinner with him,
Or an opera, or even his bed. I'd sign up to heaven
If I could be certain flesh-and-blood women were there.
If all it offers is souls, no thank you. *Five*
For the symbol at your door. It could refer
To the symbol that kept the Children of Israel alive
    When the Lord smote Egypt. May it protect you too.
    Or let it be a *high-sounding cymbal*, praising you.

94

Nine for the nine bright shiners. The book I've consulted
Says these could be the orders of angels, or the nine
Joys of Mary. I'll make them all that's by the exulted
Exalted, whether in crazy poems of mine,
Or by the Irish monks under Aidan who founded
This place; or whether the object is wife or friend,
Or flesh or spirit; or whether with the passion that sounded
In my ears as I went to sleep last night at the end
Of the First Act of *Tristan und Isolde* (thanks to the miracle
Of Walkman technology), or today's thankfulness
Of prayer at St Cuthbert's Centre, my stomach spherical
After a bacon/egg/black pudding breakfast. I press
    This ecstatic conclusion, knowing it can't go on;
    Tomorrow I'll leave; something found will be gone.

95

Ten for the ten commandments. Those enemies of sex
And faith and poems. Do you want me to keep them? How can
You not? I couldn't be a poet without some flecks,
Without at least one lapse from the seventh ban –
But in the end I'm stuck. They insist that giving
Turns into giving away, giving up; the ghost
Itself must be yielded. I return tomorrow to living
Mortally – far from the magic of isle and coast,
Back to home and job. I've squared the circle
Long enough; farewell, my tricksy spirit, *I shall miss
Thee; but yet thou shalt have freedom:* to shackle
Spirit to ourselves is fantasy at best, an abyss
   At worst; I can only hope that letting you go
   Will leave a warm, tender, affectionate glow.

96

The book I'm using for the text and meaning of the *Dilly
Song* says that *the six proud walkers* are 'those
Who bore the water-pots at the feast of Cana'. Silly.
The meaning of songs – and of these sonnets, I hope – grows
From those who enjoy them. I'm proud to be a proud
Walker. I like the stride of my boots, whether
On *Whin Sill dolerite*, hard and unbowed
After millions of years; or on bouncy heather;
Or squelching mud. I like this isle, but I love
The mainland too. I'm happy to gaze and sup
At sky and wind-fluffed clouds and all that's above
My head; but I'm glad that life's a disposable cup.
   We'll all come to nothing – so will this Whin Sill:
   Thrown away fast, when God has drunk his fill.

This book on English song annoys me. *Three,*
Three, the rivals – it says they're the Magi. Crap.
They're simply the three who have such a hold on me.
The third has been left out, but the sonnets tap
Her power as a reader – no one will understand
Them better. She's waited loyally for some expression
Of thanks. It's here, *mit lieben Grüßen.* My sand
Is running out. When its mode is naked confession,
Poetry exhausts itself. Four sonnets to go.
The end will be like death – but maybe like birth
Too. Conceivably, more than the three know,
Their gifts have brought a miracle to earth –
     So they're Magi after all. What will unfold?
     Historia Calamitatum. But it may strike gold.

98

To me, fair friend, you never can be old –
And so you count as *Two, two, the lily-white*
Boys, clothèd all in green O – with untold
Others from that company too, whose light,
Because it shines in them so brightly, helps
Us to see it in all. We have to behave,
However, as if it belongs with the barks and yelps
Of seals and the gannets' cries. It won't save
Us. Morality's a human matter. Ruin and madness
Can come from linking judgement and action to spirit.
Is the beauty of the isle beyond not only badness
But goodness? That must be so, though it's hard to believe it.
     Give. Give away. Give up what I have seen,
     Since first I saw you fresh, which yet are green.

99

Back to sad news. No need to say what.
There's always plenty of it: when it touches me personally
It's like it would be if the trees (they're green still, not
Fully autumnal) enclosing our house were totally
Steeped in tears, and all around they endlessly
Stretched, one behind another, a dripping world
Of trees, and this sole house in the middle. But actually,
For many, there is no such fellow-feeling: a dust-swirled,
Traffic-choked waste land surrounds them, and getting bleaker.
Eight for the April rainers? Many don't have the luxury
Of rain or pathos. The green is getting weaker.
I can feel it ebbing away. The whole panoply
 Of these sonnets, collapsing to an 'O',
 Filled only with what we humanly can know.

100

Four for the Gospel makers. Easy – I've just
Been to Lindisfarne. The haloes are what I took in.
Those immaculate 'O's round the heads of the four. Rust
Red round the rim of Matthew's, gold within;
Green round the gold of Mark's; nothing but gold
For Luke's; for John's, gold on the rim, then a band
Of purple, then crimson. Their robes, in colour and fold,
As varied. Who directed the artist? His hand
Was his own, welding traditions – Celtic, Roman,
Saxon. The spirit can't make such order or grace
Or goodness. I felt that last night, playing Haydn.
The 'O' is for us to fill. But if that space
 Is befitted, the spirit floods in with a golden chime –
 Delighted we've found, by ourselves, so perfect a rhyme.

101

I'm meeting you tonight. Which you? It mustn't matter.
The 'O' I'll enter will be private – a circus ring
With an audience of two. I'll laugh, I'll clown, I'll natter,
Turn somersaults perhaps. I may even raucously sing
Green grow the rushes O. What is your one O? One
Is one and all alone and evermore shall be so. But
The One will be mirrored, and between – round as the sun,
Yet empty – the 'O'. You'll watch me dance and strut;
I'll then, courteously, help you across the barrier.
The other you (still watching) will not be alarmed.
No one will be hurt. As we get merrier and merrier,
Red and green spotlights will merge into gold. Charmed,
    The One in whose image of love our love will be made
    Will graciously smile. And then the lights will fade.

Note

From Reginald Nettel, *Sing a Song of England: a Social History of Traditional Song* (London 1954):

It was Gregory the Great who sent Augustine and his forty monks to Christianize southern England in A. D. 597. They were by no means the first Christian missionaries, but musically they are of importance to us. They concentrated on King Ethelbert, won him over, and the kingdom became Christian. Such is the story; but did anyone ever change his belief in response to a royal decree? The common people would not understand Christianity as a result of the king's conversion, and in fact pagan and Christian ideas would go on until understanding was achieved; fertility rites would still go on, and divine inebriation . . . The process of education towards the acceptance of the Christian life began, and it began from the only point possible – the point where pagan and Christian thought met. One of these is supposed to be preserved in the *Dilly Song*, of which even the name is a mystery – it comes from Cornwall, and is thought to be of Celtic origin. The song is responsorial; a soloist sings the first line and the company answer with the refrain; a second soloist sings the third line and the first soloist completes the verse.

> I'll sing you one O.
> *Green grow the rushes O.*
> What is your one O?
> One is one and all alone
> And evermore shall be so.

. . . There is mystery about the symbols in the song; the riddle has to be unravelled, and that makes it attractive to learn. The song goes on:

> I'll sing you two O.
> *Green grow the rushes O.*

What are your two O?
Two, two, the lily-white boys,
Clothèd all in green O.
One is one and all alone
And evermore shall be so.

The song is cumulative. With each verse another riddle is added to the list. Altogether there are twelve. The last verse of all will therefore run:

I'll sing you twelve O.
Green grow the rushes O.
What are your twelve O?
Twelve for the twelve apostles,
Eleven for the eleven who went to heaven,
Ten for the ten commandments,
Nine for the nine bright shiners,
Eight for the eight bold rangers,*
Seven for the seven stars in the sky,
Six for the six proud walkers,
Five for the symbol at your door,
Four for the Gospel makers,
Three for the rivals,*
Two, two, the lily-white boys,
Clothèd all in green O,
One is one and all alone
And evermore shall be so.

* 'Eight for the April rainers' . . . 'Three, three, the rivals' . . . in the version I learnt as child. [W. R.]